SHIRE NATURAL H

C000083891

THE LAPWING

PETER WEAVER

CONTENTS

COVER: *A female Lapwing incubating her eggs.*

Series editors: Jim Flegg and Chris Humphries.

Copyright © 1987 by Peter Weaver. First published 1987.
Number 14 in the Shire Natural History series. ISBN 0 85263 855 8.

Set in 9 point Times roman and printed in Great Britain by C. I. Thomas & Sons (Haverfordwest) Ltd, Press Buildings, Merlins Bridge, Haverfordwest, Dyfed.

Introducing the Lapwing

The black and white twinkling and plaintive calling of a flock of Lapwings in flight are among the most distinctive sights and sounds of the countryside. Even for many people who make no claim to be bird-watchers, the Lapwing is well known and much liked. It is one of the easiest species to recognise, with its striking looks, memorable voice and distinctive habits, while its widespread occurrence on ordinary farmland ensures its familiarity to rural dwellers and visitors. So finding and watching Lapwings is not difficult, and a casual stroll through the fields may well be enlivened by encountering these most interesting and attractive birds.

Although the name 'Lapwing' is now used as standard, the alternative 'Peewit' is often preferred, echoing the basic call of the species, and other languages have their own versions of this sound, as in the Dutch *Kievit* and the German *Kiebitz*. In some parts of Britain and in Ireland the bird may be called the Green Plover, after the colour of the sheen on its dark upper parts. 'Lapwing' seems to have sprung from two Anglo-Saxon words, one meaning 'to leap' and the other 'to reel', both presumably referring to the tumbling song-flight. The scientific name of the species, *Vanellus vanellus*, is taken from a Latin word meaning 'little fan', apparently relating to the throbbing made by the male's wings in spring, and is reflected in the French name for the Lapwing, *Vanneau*.

APPEARANCE AND CALLS

Lapwings are medium-sized, averaging about 11.5 inches (29 cm) from bill to tail, with a wingspan almost three times this length. Their upper parts, although often appearing black, are dark glossy green, with a hint of blue and purple here and there. The upper sides of the wings are truly black towards their ends, but some of the longest flight feathers have whitish tips. The underparts are white, except for a black breast-band and a patch of chestnut under the tail, which has a broad black patch almost at the tip but is otherwise white, with some reddish brown feathers above its base. The face is white or buffish with black markings, and the wispy black crest is well seen at close quarters, though it is held flat in flight. The wings are black underneath with large white patches next to the body.

With practice the sexes can be told apart in the breeding season and juveniles can be separated from adults. The male has sharper facial markings, a longer crest and broader wings than his mate, while his black chin and throat lack the white mottling of the female. Outside the breeding season the sexes look similar, with their chins and throats white and their faces buffish and blurred, while their upper parts have buff fringes on some of the feathers. Juveniles resemble these winter adults, but their faces are still more indistinctly marked, their crests are very short, and their upper parts are more noticeably patterned with buff.

The voice of the Lapwing is one of its best known features, the classic 'pee-wit' call being modified according to circumstances. Variations can be used to signify anxiety, alarm, aggression or enticement. It usually sounds shrill and plaintive but can be short and sharp, quiet or far-carrying. Its most typical form is perhaps heard from birds in flocks, especially on arrival or departure. Rather different notes are heard on the breeding grounds, and the remarkable song, delivered by the male during a special and equally remarkable flight, is described in the chapter dealing with the breeding season.

RELATIVES AND DISTRIBUTION

Despite its association with dry ground, the Lapwing is a member of the group of birds known as the waders. In fact Lapwings are often found in damp places and beside water, where they can be seen wading alongside their more typical relatives. The waders of the world are divided into twelve families, and the Lapwing is a member of the second largest of these, the plover family (Charadriidae). This is split into two sub-families, the first of which contains the 'true' plovers. Six of these are regularly

1. *Heads of breeding Lapwings showing differences between male (left) and female (right). Although the exact markings vary from one individual to another, males generally have more solidly black and white patterns. The length of the crest averages about 3.5 inches (88 mm) in males and around 2.9 inches (73 mm) in females, but this distinction may be difficult to judge in the field, and at moulting time it is useless as a means of identification.*

seen in the British Isles, including the Ringed Plover of the shorelines, the Golden Plover of the moorlands and the Dotterel of the mountains. The Lapwing is the only British representative (apart from two vagrants) of the other group of plovers, often called the vanelline plovers after the scientific name of their subfamily (Vanellinae), meaning the 'Lapwing-like' birds.

The twenty-four species of vanelline plovers are mainly tropical, with ten in Africa, nine (including one not seen since 1939) in Eurasia, three in South America, two in Australasia and none in North America (apart from the Lapwings which have wandered there). One African species, the Spur-winged Plover, extends as a breeding bird into south-east Europe, and two Asian species nest on or close to the easternmost fringes of Europe. Both of these, the Sociable and White-tailed Plovers, have been recorded in Britain as vagrants, the former many times, but in Europe as a whole the only regularly occurring vanelline plover is the Lapwing.

The heartland of the Lapwing's breeding distribution lies across Eurasia between the latitudes of 50 and 60 degrees north, marking the species as essentially a bird of the temperate zone. In Europe,

however, it nests well to the north of this belt, crossing the Arctic Circle in Scandinavia and the western USSR, and in various regions the range extends south, reaching Spain, north Italy, Greece, Turkey, the Caspian Sea and northern China, with a few even breeding in northernmost Morocco. Therefore the Lapwing breeds from the edge of the Arctic tundra to the Mediterranean and meets conditions from the highly oceanic (as in Ireland) to the extremely continental (as in central Asia). The far north of Europe was colonised from the late nineteenth century onwards, a period of climatic improvement, and in 1963 breeding was first recorded in Iceland. Curiously, there has also been some expansion in southern Europe, for example in France since the 1930s and Italy since the 1960s.

The Lapwing breeds throughout the British Isles, which lie in the middle latitudes of its range, but it is thinly spread in north-west Scotland (presumably because of the rugged terrain) and in south-west Wales, Devon and Cornwall (for no obvious reason). Decreases since the 1940s in southern Britain have caused some gaps to appear and have been attributed to agricultural changes, yet the Lapwing is almost absent from south-west Ireland, where farming has retained

3

its traditional features more than in other regions. Meanwhile a spread northwards in Scotland coincided with the similar extension on the continent and so perhaps was also encouraged by a more favourable climate.

HABITAT, FOOD AND BEHAVIOUR

Although Lapwings are found in a wide variety of places from crop fields to sand dunes and from golf courses to mudflats, all their habitats must satisfy two basic requirements. Firstly, they must consist of open ground, with tall features such as trees, hedges or buildings widely scattered or, better still, absent altogether. So they avoid parkland, small fields and rocky ground, while enclosed habitats like woods and built-up areas are totally unsuitable, although there are records of nesting on flat roofs. Secondly, vegetation, if present, must not be high enough to impede walking or block the view, but this proviso is relaxed during the breeding season to some extent. Exposure to wind and rain is no problem, although Lapwings breed mainly at altitudes below 1500 feet (450 m) and they almost all winter on lower ground. Many Lapwing habitats are poorly drained, even waterlogged, but others lack surface water of any kind.

For feeding, the soil must be accessible, another reason for avoiding closely vegetated places. This factor varies through the year, hard frost or snow cover in winter and plant growth or dry weather in summer causing problems for Lapwings. In heavily populated regions such as western Europe, farmland provides the most obvious feeding opportunities for Lapwings. Grass is much favoured, meadows and rough pastures more for nesting and shorter grass (for example, in well grazed fields) more for feeding. Arable land is much used for feeding in winter, but is less suitable for breeding because of farming operations which may destroy eggs or young.

Off the farm Lapwings are attracted to such habitats as grassy heaths and moors, sports grounds, waste areas and airfields. In the last case, being relatively large birds which can occur in considerable numbers, they may pose a serious hazard to aircraft, the only instance in which the Lapwing conflicts with man's interests.

2. *Breeding distribution of the Lapwing. The species nests in the temperate zone of Eurasia, mainly between latitudes 50 and 60 degrees north, but extending well to the north and south of this zone in places, particularly in Europe, where it breeds from the Arctic Ocean to the Mediterranean. From west to east its range stretches from some Atlantic islands across Europe to the Pacific coast of Asia.*

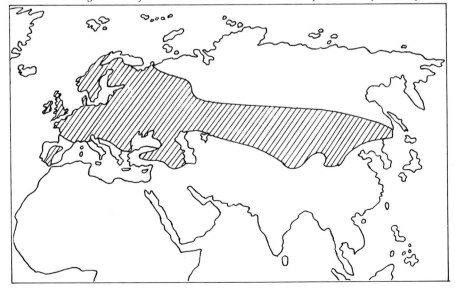

3. *An adult male Lapwing in breeding plumage: dark glossy green upper parts with a touch of purple, white underparts except for a black breast-band, wispy crest, and white face with black patterning. The black throat, cleanly marked face and long crest distinguish the male.*

4. *The female differs from the male in her mottled throat, 'dirtier' face and shorter crest. The Lapwing's large dark eye is well seen in this bird settling on to her clutch, opening the feathers of her underside to reveal the bare brood patches which warm the eggs.*

5. *The Lapwing's typical feeding method is to run a short distance, stop, peer at the ground, tilt forward and then peck. Prey is taken from the surface or just below it. The very short crest and many light fringes on the feathers of this bird's upper parts suggest that it is in its first year.*

They are also fond of wetlands, such as marshes and fens, flood meadows, freshwater margins and, along the coast, saltmarshes and mudflats. Habitat selection in the Lapwing has been intensively studied, notably through the enquiries organised by the British Trust for Ornithology in 1937 and 1960-1, but the reasons why the birds consistently return to some places, even individual fields, and ignore others which seem (to us) equally suitable, remain a mystery.

Unless it is simply a place for roosting, a habitat used by Lapwings must provide food for them. They seek mainly animal prey, but they do take in small amounts of plant material, such as grass and seeds. Small invertebrates living on or just below the surface of the soil form the bulk of their food, with insects predominating, especially beetles but also flies, grasshoppers, ants, earwigs, bugs and moths. Many of these are eaten as larvae, for example leatherjackets and wireworms (larvae of crane flies or 'daddy-long-legs' and click beetles respectively). Non-insect prey includes earthworms (which can be important in certain places at some seasons), woodlice, millipedes, spiders, molluscs (such as slugs and snails) and, among vertebrates, frogs, tadpoles and small fish. During the year an individual Lapwing is likely to take a range of food as it moves from place to place and as the seasons come and go.

The Lapwing's standard feeding method is typical of the plovers. The bird runs a little way, pauses, peers at the ground with its large dark eyes, tilts forward (as if on a hinge) and then pecks. It seems that prey can be located by ear as well as by sight, which probably explains how the Lapwing can feed at night. Sometimes, in common with certain other ground-feeding birds, it patters rapidly with its foot, perhaps to force hidden animals to move and so give themselves away.

The Lapwing runs well on its strong legs, but mainly in short bursts and at no great speed, and it spends a good deal of time standing, while searching for or dealing with prey, scanning for predators, preening, resting and so on. When anxious it stretches its neck up and may bob its head up and down or flick its tail. Lapwings do not use perches but occasionally station themselves on eminences such as molehills or mounds.

In the air the Lapwing looks like no other bird, and it can be identified from a long distance. The wing action is slow for a wader, rather jerky and appearing to be hard work. As the wing beats, the alternating black and white pattern of upper parts and underside causes a blinking or twinkling effect. Despite its rather bumbling image, the Lapwing is a strong flier and on migration can reach speeds of over 40 mph (64 km/h), comparing well with other waders. The wild song-flight shows its ability to throw itself all over the sky with breathtaking abandon, very different from its usual plodding progress.

6. *Arable land is well suited for feeding, and its bare soil is much frequented in winter, but farming operations cause hazards for breeding. On this field of sprouting barley incubation must be fitted in between rolling of the seedbed and the growth of the crop to a height which excludes Lapwings. The very open nature of the Lapwing's habitat is apparent.*

7. *Lapwings breeding on grass are more successful than those on arable land, but although grazing livestock keep the sward nicely short for feeding, slightly longer grass is preferred for nesting and animals must be lured away from eggs or young by distraction displays. This permanent pasture is used all year round by foraging Lapwings.*

Life in the flock

Lapwings are conspicuously gregarious outside the breeding season, and their flocks are a common sight on farmland in winter. Many of these are small, with perhaps a few dozen birds, but hundreds or even thousands gather in favoured places. At a given spot the size of the flock varies as birds reach and leave the area and weather conditions change. Even during a single day numbers rise and fall with arrivals and departures, as the highly mobile Lapwings range over the countryside.

The first flocks of the season can be seen as early as May, being made up of Lapwings which have failed to breed. By the end of July they are joined by successful nesters, together with the newly fledged young of the year. There is a great deal of movement at this time as birds disperse at the end of the breeding season, and some may travel long distances, for example between central Europe and Britain. A flock seen in summer, therefore, may include local birds or Lapwings from many miles away. Through autumn and into winter numbers continue to build up, perhaps reaching a peak in November or maybe later, depending on location and weather. Frost and snow will cause flocks to dwindle and, if the harsh conditions persist, to move away entirely. A gathering of over a thousand is large but not unusual, five thousand is uncommon, and more than this is rare.

Why do Lapwings form flocks? What are the benefits of this communal living? The advantages of flocking, for the Lapwing, seem to relate to improvement of feeding efficiency and reduction of the risk of attack by predators. For an individual bird, joining a flock can result in finding its way to good food supplies, simply by staying with the others and perhaps benefiting from their experience. Lapwings congregate year after year in

8. *On take-off the flash of black and white on wings, body and tail signals to a Lapwing's companions that danger may be near. In this example the whitish marks on the wingtips and the chestnut under the tail are visible but the crest is held flat in flight. The Lapwing is classified as a wader, and although it frequents dry ground it is also common in wetland habitats.*

9. *Feeding Lapwings arrange themselves fairly evenly over their foraging ground, facing in various directions unless the wind is strong. These birds are in two postures, scanning for danger and peering at the ground.*

certain places which obviously satisfy their needs, and individuals joining flocks improve their chances of discovering high-quality feeding grounds and secure roosting places. Birds in contact with others are also more likely to learn about new foraging opportunities (resulting from, for example, a field being ploughed). Even within a field the behaviour of its companions can give a bird an idea of where the most easily obtained food can be found.

The anti-predator function of flocking works on the principle of safety in numbers. A single bird has a greater chance of being caught than if it is a member of a flock, where the predator has a choice of victims. The sheer numbers of birds may even confuse the attacker, especially if they fly up. Also a flock has many eyes, and an approaching hazard is more likely to be spotted by a group than by a lone individual, and so the flock member can spend more time feeding, as it needs to spend less time scanning for danger. A number of birds of prey, notably Sparrowhawks and Peregrines, are known to take Lapwings and, at least while roosting, they are also vulnerable to ground predators such as foxes and stoats. The approach of

humans and dogs usually puts a flock to flight at some distance.

Feeding Lapwings distribute themselves fairly evenly over their foraging area, keeping perhaps about 10 feet (3 m) apart. When a flock first lands it may be quite compact, but the birds soon spread out from their point of arrival. As the Lapwings make their typical short runs there is constant movement this way and that, although they will all face into a strong wind. Occasionally they make longer runs on twinkling legs or transfer from one part of the flock to another in short, low flights. These movements may result from aggressive encounters or disturbance, and if a human intruder does not put up the whole flock the nearest birds may peel away and land further off.

Although the flock may seem well organised, its members have little to do with each other. Aggression is not very noticeable, but now and then one bird runs at another, causing it to retreat a little distance. There is some evidence of Lapwings defending feeding territories, up to about 10 feet (3 m) across, but this is unusual. At any one moment it is likely that most, if not all, of the birds in a flock will be involved in the same activity (such as foraging or resting), but in some cases

9

	J	F	M	A	M	J	J	A	S	O	N	D
FLOCKING	■	■	■	■		■	■	■	■	■	■	■
MIGRATION	■	■	■						■	■	■	
MOULT–adult		■	■			■	■	■	■			
MOULT–juvenile		■	■				■	■	■	■	■	■
SONG		■	■	■	■							
EGGS			■	■	■							
CHICKS				■	■	■	■					

10. *Lapwings spend the major part of their year in flocks, which can be seen in almost any month. Summer wanderings merge with true autumn migration in September, and winter movements in response to hard weather may grade into spring migration. The moult in February and March involves feathers of the head, neck and breast and produces the breeding plumage, while the moult of summer and autumn affects all the feathers (except in the juvenile) and leads to the non-breeding (winter) plumage. In Britain the breeding season (from arrival on the nesting grounds to dispersal of adults and young) starts in February or March and continues until July or August, though some birds may be flocking again by May or June. Although the Lapwing is single-brooded, the breeding season is extended by the laying of replacement eggs after initial losses.*

there may be sleeping birds in the middle and feeding birds towards the edges. The flocks are not particularly cohesive, and if danger threatens some birds may take off and land again, or even fly right away, without the others taking alarm, and even if the majority depart some may elect not to move at all. On other occasions the whole mass may fly up as one, with just a few alarm calls, rather than the cacophony as when a flock of geese is put up. During and after take-off the white flashes under the wings and on the tail signal to other Lapwings that danger may be near, as with the bobtail of a rabbit.

In the air flocks of Lapwings often look ragged and scrappy, with no hint of structure and with individuals or groups straggling or even pulling apart from the rest. They may seem weary and hesitant, with their slow, spasmodic flapping. At other times a flock may appear much more purposeful, the birds being more neatly arranged and the flight more rapid and direct. This more formal pattern is typical of Lapwings intending to cover a long distance, rather than just cruising around locally. Like other waders, they are capable of highly synchronised flight, well seen as a flock wheels over a field at a gradually decreasing height, checking for danger before landing. Such birds may glide down gently or they may suddenly plummet, side-slipping and almost falling out of the sky.

Resting flocks are more compact than those which are foraging, the birds arranged only about 5 feet (1.5 m) apart. They normally face upwind, often with their bills tucked into the feathers of their shoulders. Usually they sleep standing up, but sometimes they sit on the ground. The roosts are in safe places like the centres of large fields or out on mudflats, with good visibility all round, and they may also be used for feeding. Lapwings can be found resting at any time of day or night. They often feed around dawn and in the gathering dusk, while about the time of the full moon they may be active throughout the night.

A flock on the ground is an obvious attraction to birds flying over, and it may steadily grow as newcomers arrive. An actively feeding flock has clearly found a good food supply and is worth joining, provided that the field is not already saturated with Lapwings. In the latter case, extra arrivals will increase aggressive encounters and these will lower the rate of feeding, causing some birds to leave the flock in search of better foraging elsewhere. Aggression reveals an order of dominance: males over females

11. *As this flock takes to the air the Lapwings' broad black and white wings are prominent, along with the white underparts and black breast-bands. Gulls often accompany Lapwings and regularly steal prey from them.*

and adults over juveniles, which may be relegated to poorer parts of the feeding grounds. The proportion of young birds in flocks varies greatly, but 40 to 75 per cent may be typical. In early summer some flocks may be made up entirely of juveniles or of adults.

Lapwings often feed alongside other species of birds. In some cases this is purely coincidental: Woodpigeons and Skylarks, for example, may use the same fields but are seeking different foods. Rooks and Jackdaws, on the other hand, partly share the Lapwing's diet. Some species seem positively attracted to Lapwing flocks, probably using them as indicators of feeding opportunities. This is certainly the case with Golden Plovers, which frequently associate with Lapwings on the ground, though their differing styles of flight separate them in the air. Starlings, which are very often seen whizzing about within Lapwing flocks, perhaps use them in the same way. The appearance of a bird of prey usually causes a flock to take off and wheel around in tight bunches, presumably a manoeuvre intended to confuse the predator. Carrion Crows flying low over Lapwings on the ground cause the nearest birds to start into the air, although crows are not dangerous to healthy adults.

There is a special connection between

12. *Resting Lapwings keep closer together than foraging birds, and often choose watery sites for security against predators. These birds are all facing into a strong wind. Lapwings can be found roosting in daylight as well as in darkness, especially around the time of full moon, when they may feed throughout the night.*

the Lapwing and some species of gulls, chiefly the Black-headed. These birds are not simply looking for places to feed but intend to steal food from the Lapwings. They station themselves at regular intervals through the flock, standing perhaps 40 feet (12 m) apart, with a ratio of around one gull to ten or twenty Lapwings. A gull waits for a nearby Lapwing to capture an item of prey, and then flies at its victim, which usually takes off, with the gull in hot pursuit, until the prey is dropped and retrieved by the robber either in mid air or on the ground. This practice is known as 'food piracy' or 'kleptoparasitism' and has been closely studied since the 1970s. The research suggests that a gull could satisfy its daily energy needs solely by stealing food in this way.

Food piracy, however, is not easy and is not always successful. The gull must position itself so that it can reach nearby Lapwings before they have time to swallow their prey, and it needs to attack at just the right moment, when its intended victim is concentrating on grabbing the prey and is therefore fully occupied. Lapwings try to minimise losses of food to the pirates. They constantly scan their surroundings, and about half the attacks are detected before the gulls reach their targets. The Lapwings tend gradually to move away from the watching gulls, which are then forced to relocate themselves or give up. By facing away from the robbers the Lapwings can conceal their prey, though the larger items such as sizable worms are more difficult to hide and take longer to handle, so that these valuable pieces are more likely to be stolen. The risk of kleptoparasitism seems to be a disadvantage of living in flocks, but the presence of the pirates may have one benefit: the observant gulls seem to have a keen eye for possible danger, thus providing the Lapwings with an early warning system.

Break-up of winter flocks may begin about the middle of February and is well advanced by early March, when most British breeders are setting up their territories. Immigrants, however, may stay until April, as spring comes later to some of their nesting areas, and so at a given spot in, say, mid March there may be local birds already starting the breeding cycle, winter visitors still remaining and migrants passing through. Hard weather will delay return to the nesting grounds and keep birds in their flocks, but normally by the beginning of April the largest gatherings to be seen are a few birds on 'neutral ground' outside established territories. Only a few weeks later, however, at the end of May, the first signs of the new flocking season might appear, such is the Lapwing's desire for social life when not occupied with breeding duties.

13. *A female incubating her eggs at a typical nest site in rough grass. Nests can sometimes be found by scanning a field for sitting birds, which may be clearly visible if the vegetation is short. Incubation lasts for three to four weeks.*

14. *A male taking his turn at incubation. Although his mate takes the major share the male may cover the eggs for short periods during the daytime. As the grass grows the incubating bird may become completely concealed. This is another typical nest site, in boggy conditions.*

15. *This nest on a field of emerging barley has a substantial lining and a normal clutch of eggs. Arranged with their points facing inwards, they are secure in the nest cup. Nests are completely unconcealed but the colour and markings of the eggs form an effective camouflage. The hard nodule of soil which has found its way into the nest is unlikely to be ejected, such solid objects apparently being treated as eggs.*

The breeding season

Lapwings return to their breeding grounds from February onwards, depending on their location and, within each year, on weather conditions. The males tend to arrive first, and for a few days they may associate in groups, but it soon becomes obvious that their desire for each other's company is waning, and the increasingly frequent quarrels lead to the birds gradually spacing themselves out into territories.

Once a male has decided which part of the nesting area he wants as his own he must keep other males off it, and he ensures that his presence is duly noted by performing a special song-flight. In both its visual and vocal elements this show of strength is bound to attract attention. The male takes off and flies near the ground with slow exaggerated flapping, and then he speeds up, rolling from side to side on throbbing wings and zigzagging this way and that, gaining height before suddenly diving and then rising again. The flight continues more slowly and nearer the ground but then comes the most dramatic part, beginning with a sudden steep climb and the start of the song itself. The high-level section which follows ends abruptly with a roll over and a vertical dive during which the song is completed. He pulls out of his headlong plunge close to the ground and wobbles and weaves for a little distance before either landing or repeating all or part of his performance. The details vary between individuals and according to circumstances. The song has always chal-

16. *The male beats the bounds of his territory in a spectacular song-flight, during which he wobbles, zigzags, rolls and dives while singing. Here he is plunging towards the ground in full cry, advertising his ownership of the territory to neighbouring males.*

14

17. *Rival males, as well as facing up to each other on the ground, engage in aerial disputes along their territorial boundaries, chasing and diving on each other or flying side by side. The males' very broad wings, which produce a deep throbbing sound during part of the song-flight, are much in evidence in this view of a chase.*

lenged writers of bird books to put it into words, and K. G. Spencer, in his standard work on the Lapwing (1953), suggests the following version: 'ayhrre-wil-luch-o-weep, weep, weep; eyuweep'. No description, however, can convey the excitement and exuberance of either the flight or the song, an exhilarating audio-visual combination which lifts the heart at the end of winter.

Males practise their song-flights even before they establish their territories, and from this diffident start these advertising displays grow in length and intensity as the birds define their property rights. The male beats the bounds of his patch during the flight, following a roughly oval course back to his base. Many performances are sparked off by the appearance of a rival, while others have no obvious trigger. They reach a peak about egg-laying time and then decline, ceasing at hatching, when territorial boundaries break down.

There are also confrontations between males on the ground, which run at each other in hunched postures, flicking their

tails, raising their wings above their backs, or standing face to face with breasts thrust out to emphasise their black gorgets. As a gesture of appeasement the back is turned and the body tilted forwards to display the chestnut undertail coverts to the opponent. Many of these disputes take to the air, either as song-flights or as contests in which each bird strives to rise above the other and then dive on it, sometimes striking it with an audible thump. Males may also fly side by side or chase each other along a hotly disputed border zone.

What is the point of all this aggression? Why do Lapwings use up so much energy in establishing and defending territories? Although they frequently nest in what could be called loose colonies, they still feel the need to space themselves out quite widely. Size of territories varies greatly, perhaps averaging between 1 and 2 acres (0.4 to 0.8 ha), and these differences seem to be at least partly related to food supply, with smaller territories if feeding is easier. Some Lapwings, however, leave their territories to feed on 'neutral ground' and may take their young there as well, so provision of a private hunting preserve cannot be the only function of territory, even though many Lapwings do feed only within their own boundaries. Perhaps territories are set up for a number of reasons, which might include adequate spacing of nests and provision of a haven for courtship as well as (in some cases) security with regard to food supply.

Once established in his domain, the male needs to attract a mate, as partners go their separate ways at the end of each breeding season and Lapwings do not normally pair up in the winter flocks. The song flights may help to attract females to territories, and they may visit several before deciding where to settle. Early in the season males display by gently rocking their bodies up and down with their backs to the females, flashing their chestnut undertail coverts, but as sexual activity intensifies the 'scrape display' becomes the fundamental element of courtship. The male lowers himself on to his breast, and then squirms and kicks backwards, while wagging his tail up and down at the female. These actions form a little hollow in the ground, up to twenty of which may be made, some without a female even being present. Copulation often precedes or follows scraping, the male commonly flying straight on to the female's back.

The interest taken by the female in the male's endeavours depends on how far her own breeding condition has progressed. If she is receptive she will join in the scraping after a few days, whereas previously she had simply stood and watched. The scrape at which she works will become the actual nest and within a day should contain the first egg. The site varies greatly but is out in the open with no deliberate concealment and may be on a slight elevation, such as a small mound or low ridge, especially in damp places. A good view all round may be sought, but growth of vegetation may obstruct the outlook before incubation is over. The cup for the eggs is about 5 inches (13 cm) across, and both sexes line it with small pieces of plant material, the amount used varying from hardly any to quite a bulky mass, with additions made after incuba-

tion has begun.

Lapwings' eggs have a shape which is typical of those laid by waders, being broad at one end and rather pointed at the other, reducing the risk of them rolling out of the nest. Their ground colour is usually a shade of brown or olive, sometimes tending towards umber or buff, and more rarely bluish, greenish or reddish. They have a variable number of black blotches and spots, often heavier towards the broad end, and their colouration and markings camouflage them well under most conditions. They average almost 1.9 inches (47 mm) in length and measure about 1.3 inches (33 mm) across. Most clutches contain four eggs, but there are sometimes only three and occasionally two or five. If the eggs are lost, the female can produce replacements within a fortnight, or even a week, but these are not laid in the original nest. In Britain the first clutches are seen in late March, while some replacements may still be unhatched in mid June.

Incubation lasts for three or four weeks, both sexes participating but the female taking the greater share and usually covering the eggs at night. The male mainly stands guard, ready to warn the sitting female of approaching danger. Both birds may fly up and attack aerial predators like birds of prey and crows, but in the early stages of incubation a human intruder simply causes the incubating bird to leave the nest quietly and fly to a point from which it can watch until the danger has passed. Instead of flying straight back to the nest, it lands some distance away and then walks, sometimes pretending to feed, as if there were no nest there at all. As hatching time approaches, and when the young are small, the male rises to greet an intruder and flies around calling with a harsh two-syllabled note, often joined by his mate and even neighbouring birds. Humans may be subjected to diving attacks, without physical contact being made, while bird or mammal predators are chased or lured away from the vicinity, though Lapwings seldom perform the elaborate distraction displays practised by some other waders. Farm livestock, which may trample nests or young, also needs to be side-tracked.

16

In Britain the eggs hatch from late April onwards, all the young in a given brood emerging within a day or so. Unlike those of songbirds, wader chicks are alert and active as soon as they hatch, covered with down and able to run and even swim. The newly hatched Lapwing is a beautiful creature, with buffish brown upper parts quite heavily mottled with black, except for a pure white nape, the function of which is probably to signal the exact whereabouts of the chick to its parents. The underparts are white, but even at this early age a blackish breast-band is present. The young can feed themselves from the beginning, pecking at small moving objects within a few hours of hatching. For the first day or two they stay close to the nest, but subsequently the parents may lead them right out of the area, even across roads and streams, enticing the chicks forward by calling to them. As before the hatch, the male chiefly stands guard, while his mate looks after the young, brooding them frequently during the first week and at night for a week longer. If they become scattered, she calls them together with a quiet version of the 'peewit' note. If danger threatens, she uses a harsher call,

18. *The Lapwing chick is fully alert, mobile and able to feed right from hatching. Its mottled upper parts and white underside have a disruptive effect, breaking up its outline and thus concealing it as it crouches motionless when danger threatens. The blackish breast-band is already apparent, and the white nape may signal the whereabouts of the chick to the adults. Even tiny young have strong legs and feet and well formed bills.*

and the chicks then crouch, hiding their white napes, and freeze into immobility, often becoming almost invisible as the pattern of their down breaks up their outlines. They remain crouching until the female's soft call signals that all is clear.

Within a fortnight of hatching, the chick's down is beginning to be replaced by its first covering of feathers, and it starts to develop the appearance and mannerisms of the adult. Young Lapwings fly at about five or six weeks old, though they remain with their parents for a few days longer. By this time, however, some pairs have already split up, especially if it is late in the season. The youngsters modify their original juvenile plumage by moulting some of their new feathers in the late summer or autumn, and they are then best described as 'first-winter' birds. Meanwhile, from May or June to August or September, the adults are moulting into their non-breeding plumage, which they will keep until February or March. As the reproductive cycle winds down in the early summer heat, both parents and young are absorbed into the developing flocks, and the longer phase of the Lapwing's year has begun.

What are the results of all the time and effort expended on the song-flights, the border disputes, the courtship rituals, the incubation of the eggs and the rearing of the chicks? The majority of the eggs hatch, but the majority of the young die before fledging. Eggs and chicks are taken by predators such as crows, gulls and foxes or are destroyed, albeit accidentally, by man's activities. Some eggs are infertile, and some young fail to survive cold, wet weather. Ringing returns suggest that by the end of the winter 37 per cent of the young fledged during the previous year are dead, and that a third of the adults die each year, giving an adult a further life expectancy of 2½ years. As Lapwings do not normally breed until their second spring, and as they nest only once a year but replace lost clutches, it has been suggested that to keep the population stable each pair must produce about 1½ young in a season. An estimated 200,000 or more Lapwings breed in the British Isles, although numbers are reduced by hard winters.

Lapwings on the move

Although Lapwings are not world travellers like some of their fellow waders, most of their populations are migratory, moving in some cases up to 2500 miles (4000 km). British breeders have some degree of choice, the maritime climate ensuring that winters are seldom hard enough to cause serious problems, but away from the moderating influence of the Atlantic circumstances are very different. Lapwings nesting from Scandinavia and central Europe eastwards are forced to migrate south or west to escape the frosts and snow which prevent the birds from finding food.

The first movements of the season, however, take place surprisingly early, beginning in May or June. They involve birds from central Europe, which fly west or north-west into Holland and Britain or south-west into southern France or Italy, while from the Baltic area Lapwings head south-west to Denmark, north Germany and Britain. These movements continue through the summer to merge with the true autumn migration, and their cause is uncertain. Perhaps the warm, dry summers of their regions of origin bake the ground hard and so impede feeding, but a further puzzle is the small number of juveniles involved, these early travellers being chiefly adults.

The autumn migration proper begins in September, and by this time young of the year, with their short crests and scaly upper parts, are prominent in the flocks on the move. The birds tend to wait until the first hard frosts or snowstorms occur and then leave suddenly in large numbers, usually by October in Scandinavia and the USSR and by November in more westerly and southerly parts of Europe. Scandinavian Lapwings head south-west along the continental coast of the North Sea and on into France, the Iberian peninsula and even north-west Africa. Some cross the North Sea into Britain, where they are joined by birds from Holland and north Germany. Some Russian Lapwings also reach the North Sea,

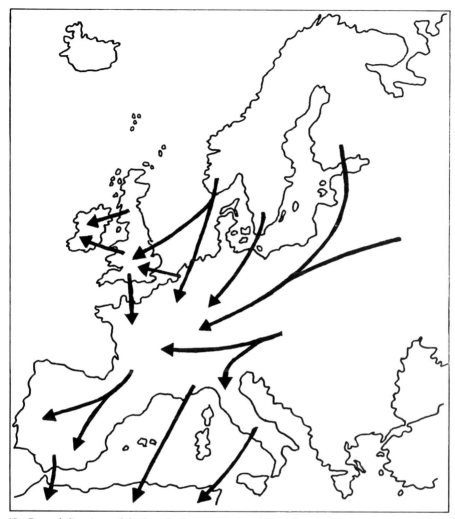

19. *General directions of the Lapwing's autumn migration in Europe. The basic pattern involves movement of north and central European birds towards France, with some crossing to the British Isles and others reaching Iberia, Italy and North Africa. In cold winters more Lapwings reach the southern destinations, while those already in Britain may move on to Ireland, France or beyond.*

but most combine with those from central Europe to reach France, Iberia, Italy and perhaps North Africa.

Some British breeders stay more or less in their home areas, while others move some distance and more leave Britain. High ground is deserted, and there is a generally southerly or south-westerly shift of Scottish and northern English birds. Ireland is a popular resort for these British migrants, as it usually has milder winters than Britain, and many continental Lapwings also end up in Ireland after passing through Britain. Not surprisingly Lapwings from southern Britain are less likely to move than those from the north, and if they do leave the country they tend to fly south into France and Iberia rather

20. *A Lapwing flock in flight is a mass of twinkling black and white as the dark upper parts and white underparts of the birds are alternately displayed during the slow wing flaps. Although often seen in shapeless and straggling agglomerations, Lapwings on long journeys fly more rapidly and directly in more formal groups.*

21. *Snow and frost cause problems for Lapwings by sealing their food into the ground, causing movements which may take birds to the kinder conditions of the coasts or out of Britain altogether. In these resting birds the blurred buffish faces and the buff fringes on the feathers of their dark green upper parts are the marks of the non-breeding plumage.*

than west into Ireland. Further complexities arise from differences in the behaviour of adults and first-winter birds. The latter are slightly less ready to move outside Britain than their parents, and those which opt to do so prefer France and Iberia to Ireland, tending also to move further than the adults. The Swiss ornithologist Dr Christoph Imboden, who has made a detailed study of the migration of the Lapwing in Europe, has calculated that on average among British-bred Lapwings 33 per cent of first-years and 30 per cent of adults remain in Britain during winter, 22 per cent and 35 per cent respectively move to Ireland, and 45 per cent and 35 per cent respectively migrate to the continent.

22. *Winter quarters of European Lapwings. The map shows regions where substantial numbers of Lapwings may be encountered between autumn and spring. The south-westerly and southerly bias reflects the milder winters of the Atlantic and Mediterranean parts of Europe, where the relative lack of frost and snow ensures that the soil surface usually remains open for the birds to feed. Except during abnormally cold seasons, as in 1962-3, the British Isles form the northernmost important wintering grounds for Lapwings.*

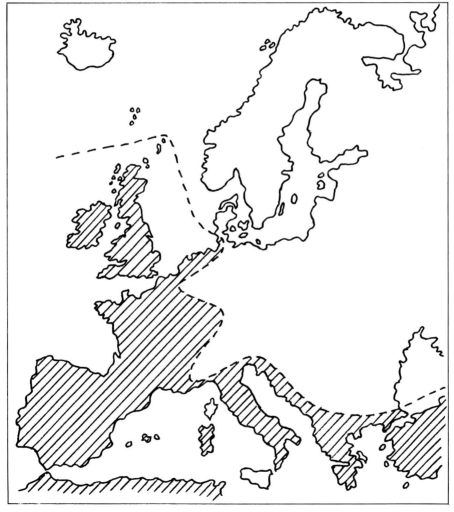

The British Isles form the most northerly important wintering ground for Lapwings, probably accommodating well over a million of them each year. Central England holds the largest numbers, with plenty also in southern and eastern England and in Ireland. Northern parts are less favoured, although Orkney, the central lowlands of Scotland and the Solway and Tyne areas are not short of wintering Lapwings. When a spell of hard weather occurs, two kinds of movement become apparent. Firstly, there is a shift towards the coasts, where the mudflats and marshes are less likely to freeze than the inland fields, and secondly there is a westerly movement which may ultimately take the birds to Ireland or a southerly one which may lead to France or beyond. How far Lapwings travel, and how long they stay away, depends on the duration and the severity of the hard weather.

During the exceptionally cold winter of 1962-3 hardly any Lapwings were left in Britain by late January, most having fled to Ireland, France or Iberia. In Iberia numbers were far higher than usual, and in this connection it is notable that the Spanish name for the Lapwing, *Avefria*, means 'bird of the cold'. Even in an ordinary winter, weather movements of Lapwings are common and conspicuous, as the birds shift their ground with the onset of bad conditions and return when temperatures rise again. Very prolonged hard weather, however, can virtually deprive Britain of its Lapwings for the rest of the winter, as happened in 1962-3. The moving birds do not always end up where they intended. Strong easterly winds may carry them past Ireland right across the Atlantic, as in December 1927, when hundreds arrived in eastern Canada, including one which had been ringed as a chick in Cumbria.

The spring return to the breeding grounds begins in late January in southern Europe and is at its height in March. The general movement simply reverses the predominantly south-westerly direction of autumn, but there is a greater sense of urgency and Scandinavian and east European birds fly more directly across the continent. Adults travel in advance of first-years, time of arrival in the nesting area depending on its location, ranging from mid February in Britain, Holland and Germany to late April in Finland. Most Lapwings (70 per cent) return to breed within a dozen or so miles (20 km) of the place in which they were hatched, but the rest may settle hundreds or even thousands of miles away, one British-bred bird being found in the USSR in May 2730 miles (4370 km) from its point of origin. This tendency to wander may explain why Lapwings look the same right across their range from Ireland to China, so that no subspecies (races) can be recognised.

The Lapwing and the farmer

Every year members of the British Trust for Ornithology collect field data for the Common Birds Census, which provides annual breeding population indices for sixty species. In 1984 the index for the Lapwing stood at 142, meaning that there were then 1.42 times more Lapwings on the census plots than in the datum year of 1966, when the indices were set at 100. This may seem very satisfactory, but a closer look reveals a less rosy picture. The figure for 1984 was almost identical to the average for the previous ten years, so instead of increasing the Lapwing is holding steady. The rise since 1966 took place before 1970, when the index value was 167, and was part of the gradual recovery from the effects of the cold winter of 1962-3, which pushed the figure right down to 87. The worrying point is the fact that the present average is well below the index for 1962 (196), which was the last year before the hard winter and also the first year of the census. On this evidence, something seems to have prevented the Lapwing from making a full recovery from that winter.

Despite the ability of Lapwings to move long distances, a widespread and total freeze is bound to affect them seriously, and it has been suggested that